Student Worktext

Cursive

ISBN#: 0-936785-44-6
TL#: HWSWTF201001

Published by The Concerned Group, Inc.
700 East Granite • P.O. Box 1000 • Siloam Springs, AR 72761

Authors **Carol Ann Retzer, Eva Hoshino**
Publisher **Russ L. Potter, II**
Senior Editor **Bill Morelan**
Project Director **Kristin Aloha**
Creative Director **Daniel Potter**
Research Asst. **Marklyn Retzer**
Proofreader **Becky Kinzey**
Illustrations **Rob Harrell & Josh Ray**
Colorists **Josh & Aimee Ray**

Scripture translation selected for appropriate vocabulary level.
All verses are taken from *The Living Bible*, Tyndale House Publishers,
Wheaton, Illinois 60187. Used by permission.

printed on recycled paper

For more information about A Reason For Handwriting®, **A Reason For Spelling**®,
A Reason For Science®, & **A Reason For Guided Reading**®, write to the address
above or visit our website.

www.AReasonFor.com

Please, Help Us Hold Down Costs!

Attention Parents & Teachers:

Don't Settle for HALF a Curriculum!

A Reason For Handwriting® **Student Worktexts** integrate faith and learning by featuring lessons based on Scripture verses and built-in opportunities for sharing God's Word with others.

But, the **A Reason For Handwriting®** curriculum offers much, much more!

The **Comprehensive K-6th Teacher Guidebook** is full of essential instructions, helpful tips, and teacher-tested techniques to help you make the most of your handwriting practice.

Key instructional information in the **Teacher Guidebook** includes:

- **The Suggested Weekly Schedule**
- **Daily Lesson Plans**
- **Tips for Teaching Cursive Handwriting**
- **Techniques for Grading**

Plus the **Teacher Guidebook** includes a wealth of teacher-tested tips and enrichment ideas:

- **A Comprehesive Skills Index**
- **Extended Activities**
- **Ways to Share Border Sheets**
- **Letter Formation Charts**
- **Tips for Proper Positioning**
- **Letter Group Charts**
- **Vocabulary Lists**
- **Common Handwriting Problems**
- **Black Line Masters**

To order the **A Reason For Handwriting®** K-6th Teacher Guidebook that goes with this **Student Worktext**, contact your curriculum supplier or call 800.447.4332

Or go to:
www.areasonfor.com

Just For Kids!

Welcome to
A Reason For Handwriting®

This year you'll learn to write better, memorize Scripture, share God's Word, and have FUN!

Each week you'll practice letters and groups of letters from a different Scripture verse. Then you'll write the entire verse on practice paper. At the end of each week you'll pick a Scripture Border Sheet from the back of your Worktext,

Parker

Susan

Rodney

write the verse in your very best handwriting, and use your creative talents to color and decorate it. Now comes the really FUN part: Sharing God's Word!

You can share God's Word, in your very own handwriting, by giving people your finished Scripture Border Sheets! You can take them to nursing homes, share them with friends, make placemats for your kitchen table, mail them to someone who isn't feeling well. . . you get the idea. And we're sure you'll come up with even more ideas throughout the year!

And sharing God's Word with others gives you the very best reason for improving your handwriting!

Meet New Friends

Throughout this book, you'll see illustrations of kids like you who are caring, sharing, working, and learning. Be sure to watch for these new faces!

Greg

Rachel

Jared

Kess

Alli

How to Become A Five Star Student!

Do you want your writing to look its very best? Here are the five basic areas you should consider when evaluating your handwriting form:

Alignment
Each letter or word should sit on the line, not above or below it.

Slant
The letter slant should be uniform and consistent. (To help you determine direction, draw a top-to-bottom line straight down the middle of each letter in a sentence.)

Size
Capital letters are all one full space tall. The lowercase letters b, d, f, h, k, l, and t are also one space tall. All other lowercase letters are half a space tall. Also, any letter that goes below the line should extend for half a space.

Shape
Letters should be consistent and easy to read. Minor differences from the model are okay, but all your letters must be formed with the proper strokes to avoid developing bad habits.

Spacing
Letters should be clearly identifiable. They should not run into each other, or be too far apart. Each word should be separated from the next word. Remember, a little more space is needed between sentences than between words.

Follow these guidelines, focusing on consistency and quality, and you'll be a **Five Star** student!

The following practice sentence contains all the letters of the alphabet:

God created zebras and foxes to walk, jump, and hide very quickly.

To The Teacher

Before beginning instruction, please review the
Weekly Lesson Format (Teacher Guidebook, page 56).

Here you will find detailed directions for implementing
the 5-day format, as well as suggestions for using the
Scripture Border Sheets.

Careful review of this material at the start of the school year
will greatly enhance the effectiveness of this curriculum.

TIP OF THE WEEK

A good goal for this year is to improve your handwriting
as you share God's Word with others. Review the **Five Star**
evaluation (page 6) with your teacher to see how you measure up.

Day One Practice the following letters and words from this week's Scripture.

A a

about

loyal

always

Day Two Continue practicing letters and words from this week's Scripture.

U u

true

born

brother

Nn

need

friend

nagging

Day Four   Practice this week's entire Scripture verse by tracing over each of the words below.

Love forgets mistakes; nagging about them parts the best of friends. A true friend is always loyal, and a brother is born to help in time of need.

Proverbs 17:9,17

FOR DISCUSSION

List the characteristics of a good friend. What things on this list describe you? How can you be a better friend?

TIP OF THE WEEK

Make certain your lowercase *e*'s and *i*'s
are easily distinguishable. When poorly written,
these two letters account for many spelling errors.

Day One Practice the following letters and words from this week's Scripture.

Dd

Despise

succeed

find

Day Two Continue practicing letters and words from this week's Scripture.

Gg

God's

spring

trouble

Ww

Word

water

mountain

Day Four Practice this week's entire Scripture verse by tracing over each of the words below.

Despise God's Word and find
yourself in trouble. Obey it and
succeed. The advice of a wise man
reflects like water from a
mountain spring.
Proverbs 13:13, 14

FOR DISCUSSION

List some ways you can share God's Word with others. How can this help you succeed in life?

12

TIP OF THE WEEK

For a car to drive smoothly, its wheels must be
in proper alignment. Smooth handwriting requires proper
alignment, too. Make sure your letters are on the line, not above or below it.

Day One Practice the following letters and words from this week's Scripture.

Hh

How

taught

mother

Day Two Continue practicing letters and words from this week's Scripture.

Tt

The

first

step

L l

Lord

fools

Listen

Day Four   Practice this week's entire Scripture verse by tracing over each of the words below.

How does a man become wise?
The first step is to trust and
reverence the Lord! Only fools
refuse to be taught. Listen to your
father and mother.
Proverbs 1:7,8

FOR DISCUSSION

How do we learn to trust someone?
What does trusting God really mean?

📚 **TIP OF THE WEEK**

Your name is the most important word you write.
Write it with care on every paper you turn in. Even though
your signature is unique, you should avoid unnecessary tails and frills.

Day One   Practice the following letters and words from this week's Scripture.

Cc

child

acts

character

Day Two   Continue practicing letters and words from this week's Scripture.

Ee

even

cheating

whether

Rr

right

every

pure

The Lord despises every kind
of cheating. The character of even
a child can be known by the
way he acts—whether what he
does is pure and right.
Proverbs 20:10,11

FOR DISCUSSION

How do your actions reflect your character?
Give at least two examples.

Name _____

TIP OF THE WEEK

The capital letters *J*, *Y*, and *Z* fill the
whole letter space. Make certain these letters
touch the top line, and descend to the lower base line.

Day One Practice the following letters and words from this week's Scripture.

Jj

Just

father

punishes

Day Two Continue practicing letters and words from this week's Scripture.

Mm

make

him

delights

Yy

you

corrects

son

Day Four Practice this week's entire Scripture verse by tracing over each of the words below.

Just as a father punishes a son
he delights in to make him better,
so the Lord corrects you.
Proverbs 3:12

FOR DISCUSSION

Are there bad ways to punish someone? Are there good ways? Discuss the difference.

Name _____

Lesson 6

TIP OF THE WEEK

The capitals *I* and *Q* are both upswing
letters, just like the capital *J*. As you practice these
letters this week, try to use the same slant for each one.

Day One   Practice the following letters and words from this week's Scripture.

Ii

It

insist

fight

Day Two   Continue practicing letters and words from this week's Scripture.

O o

Only

honor

out

Q q

quarreling

stay

man

Day Four Practice this week's entire Scripture verse by tracing over each of the words below.

It is an honor for a man to stay out of a fight. Only fools insist on quarreling.

Proverbs 20:3

FOR DISCUSSION
Is fighting always a physical thing? List some good techniques for avoiding a fight.

Tip of the week

This week, check the size of your letters.
Using consistent size will make your letters
look great, and your handwriting much easier to read.

Day One Practice the following letters and words from this week's Scripture.

Ff

For

fear

wisdom

Day Two Continue practicing letters and words from this week's Scripture.

Bb

basic

reverence

results

Kk

Knowing

kind

understanding

Day Four Practice this week's entire Scripture verse by tracing over each of the words below.

For the reverence and fear of God are basic to all wisdom. Knowing God results in every other kind of understanding.
Proverbs 9:10

FOR DISCUSSION

What does the word "fear" mean in this verse? How does knowing God result in deeper understanding?

TIP OF THE WEEK

This week's focus letters are the "boatstroke" capitals
T and *S*. Boatstroke capitals are not joined to the rest of the word.
Can you identify the other boatstroke capitals? (Hint: There are four more.)

Day One *Practice the following letters and words from this week's Scripture.*

Tt

Telling

hitting

with

Day Two *Continue practicing letters and words from this week's Scripture.*

Xx

axe

harmful

wounding

Day Three Practice the final letters and words from this week's Scripture.

Ss

sword

shooting

sharp

Day Four Practice this week's entire Scripture verse by tracing over each of the words below.

Telling lies about someone is as harmful as hitting him with an axe, or wounding him with a sword, or shooting him with a sharp arrow.

Proverbs 25:18

FOR DISCUSSION

How are lies and criticism of others harmful? What is the opposite approach?

Name _____

TIP OF THE WEEK

Bridges connect one bank of the river to the other. "Bridgestrokes" help us connect one part of a word to another. This week's bridgestroke letters are *b*, *o*, *v*, and *w*.

Day One Practice the following letters and words from this week's Scripture.

A a

away

hands

idles

Day Two Continue practicing letters and words from this week's Scripture.

P p

prosperity

better

dirty

Vv

starve

proud

work

Day Four   Practice this week's entire Scripture verse by tracing over each of the words below.

It is better to get your hands dirty—and eat, than to be too proud to work and starve. Hard work means prosperity. Only a fool idles away his time.

Proverbs 12:9, 11

FOR DISCUSSION

What are some ways people foolishly idle away their time? Name some situations where hard work can really pay off.

Name _____

📖 TIP OF THE WEEK

As you practice the capital and lowercase _Z_ this
week, watch for their similarities and differences. Can you
identify other similar letter pairs? (Hint: there are at least six more.)

Day One — Practice the following letters and words from this week's Scripture.

Zz

lazy

ways

winter

Day Two — Continue practicing letters and words from this week's Scripture.

Tt

Take

gathering

ants

27

L l

Learn

fellow

lesson

Take a lesson from the ants, you lazy fellow. Learn from their ways and be wise! They labor hard all summer, gathering food for the winter.

Proverbs 6:6, 8

FOR DISCUSSION

What did Solomon mean when he told us to learn from the ants? What are some other lessons we can learn from nature?

TIP OF THE WEEK

Posture and paper position make a big difference.

Make sure your feet are flat on the floor, and your back is straight.

Lean slightly forward, with your paper slanted in the direction of your writing arm.

Day One   Practice the following letters and words from this week's Scripture.

Ff

From

healthful

careful

Day Two   Continue practicing letters and words from this week's Scripture.

Pp

persuasive

speech

comes

Kk

Kind

like

enjoyable

Day Four Practice this week's entire Scripture verse by tracing over each of the words below.

From a wise mind comes
careful and persuasive speech. Kind
words are like honey—enjoyable
and healthful.

Proverbs 16:23, 24

FOR DISCUSSION

List some ways we can make our words "like honey." Make an extra effort to talk softly and kindly this week.

Lesson 12

📖 TIP OF THE WEEK

Here's a way to check your slant: Draw a line
top-to-bottom through the downstrokes. If your slant is
consistent, the lines will be parallel. How does *your* slant measure up?

Day One Practice the following letters and words from this week's Scripture.

Yy

Your

destroyed

soul

Day Two Continue practicing letters and words from this week's Scripture.

Nn

nourished

own

cruel

Rr

reward

are

forever

Day Four Practice this week's entire Scripture verse by tracing over each of the words below.

Your own soul is nourished when you are kind; it is destroyed when you are cruel. the good man's reward lasts forever.

Proverbs 11:17, 18

FOR DISCUSSION

Discuss the concept of "random acts of kindness."
Watch for such opportunities at school this week.
Remember, your kind act is a secret!
Don't let anyone know!

Name _____

TIP OF THE WEEK

This week's verse contains all the lowercase oval
letters (*a, c, d, g, o, p* and *q*). Make certain they
are well-rounded, and that the oval portion fills the letter space.

Day One   Practice the following letters and words from this week's Scripture.

Cc

cause

discouragement

answer

Day Two   Continue practicing letters and words from this week's Scripture.

Gg

Gentle

griping

brings

Q q

quarrels

harsh

soft

Day Four   Practice this week's entire Scripture verse by tracing over each of the words below.

A soft answer turns away wrath, but harsh words cause quarrels. Gentle words cause life and health; griping brings discouragement.

Proverbs 15:1,4

FOR DISCUSSION

Think of a situation where there were critical or harsh words. Now imagine that same scene with positive, kind words. Describe the difference between the two.

Name _____

Tip of the Week

How you hold your pencil when you write is very
important! If your wrist gets tired while writing, you may be holding
your pencil too tightly. Move your wrist in a circular motion to relax your hand.

Day One Practice the following letters and words from this week's Scripture.

Ee

Everyone

time

advice

Day Two Continue practicing letters and words from this week's Scripture.

Jj

enjoys

upward

giving

Oo

wonderful

road

godly

Day Four   Practice this week's entire Scripture verse by tracing over each of the words below.

Everyone enjoys giving good advice, and how wonderful it is to be able to say the right thing at the right time! The road of the godly leads upward.

— Proverbs 15:23, 24

FOR DISCUSSION

Can you think of a story or situation where someone said "the right thing at the right time"? Describe it.

Name _____

TIP OF THE WEEK
Putting a hyphen between two words can modify
their meaning. Look at this week's hyphenated words. What is
the meaning of each separate word? How does the hyphen change the meaning?

Day One Practice the following letters and words from this week's Scripture.

Ss

slow

is

self-control

Day Two Continue practicing letters and words from this week's Scripture.

Uu

famous

army

than

Uv

have

slow-tempered

control

Day Four   Practice this week's entire Scripture verse by tracing over each of the words below.

It is better to be slow-tempered than famous; it is better to have self-control than to control an army.

Proverbs 16:32

FOR DISCUSSION

List some situations that might give an opportunity to demonstrate self-control. How can we learn to become "slow-tempered"?

Name _____

TIP OF THE WEEK

Punctuation often changes the meaning of a sentence.
This week's verse contains many types of punctuation. Can you
name and correctly use each type? (Hint: Five types of punctuation are used.)

Day One   Practice the following letters and words from this week's Scripture.

Ww

When

wrong

breaking

Day Two   Continue practicing letters and words from this week's Scripture.

Cc

face

seems

means

Yy

everything

gloomy

glad

Day Four   Practice this week's entire Scripture verse by tracing over each of the words below.

A happy face means a glad heart; a sad face means a breaking heart. When a man is gloomy, everything seems to go wrong; when he is cheerful everything seems right!

Proverbs 15:13, 15

FOR DISCUSSION

What does the phrase "look on the bright side" mean? How can our outlook affect our attitude?

Name _____

TIP OF THE WEEK

The capital *B*, *P*, and *R* all have the
same forward-oval stroke. Focus on making
this common stroke the same as you write each letter.

Day One Practice the following letters and words from this week's Scripture.

Bb

Be

bones

basket

Day Two Continue practicing letters and words from this week's Scripture.

Pp

patient

apples

tongue

Rr

break

hard

Timely

Timely advice is as lovely as golden apples in a silver basket. Be patient and you will finally win, for a soft tongue can break hard bones.

— Proverbs 25:11,15

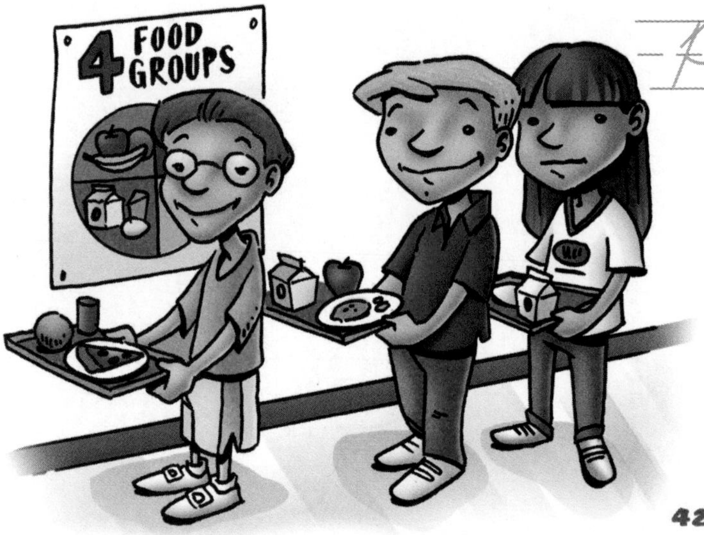

FOR DISCUSSION

What are some ways that patience can benefit us? How can we learn to be more patient?

Name _____

TIP OF THE WEEK

All the lowercase tall letters are contained in this
verse. Make certain that these letters all touch the top line.
Also, notice that two of these letters are written without loops.

Day One Practice the following letters and words from this week's Scripture.

Dd

Don't

and

dime

Day Two Continue practicing letters and words from this week's Scripture.

Ff
flow

foot

fools

43

Zz
dozen

sensible

putting

Don't talk so much. You keep
putting your foot in your mouth.
Be sensible and turn off the flow...
The words of fools are a dime
a dozen.

Proverbs 10:19, 20

FOR DISCUSSION
Do others think you talk too much, or
not enough? What do your parents and
friends think? What are some ways we
can regulate our speech?

44

Name _____

TIP OF THE WEEK

For more efficient writing, remember to dot the
i's and cross the *t*'s and *x*'s *after* you've written
the entire word. This will make your writing smoother.

Day One Practice the following letters and words from this week's Scripture.

Tt

Telling

Truth

test

Day Two Continue practicing letters and words from this week's Scripture.

Xx

exposed

gives

blessings

A a

great

many

satisfaction

Telling the truth gives a man great satisfaction, and hard work returns many blessings to him. Truth stands the test of time; lies are soon exposed.

— Proverbs 12:14, 19

FOR DISCUSSION

Can you "tell the truth" even without speaking?
What do your actions say? Give examples.

TIP OF THE WEEK

Critique a classmate's paper this week, using the
Five Star evaluation on page 6 (letter alignment, shape, size,
slant and spacing). Be sure your critique is kind and constructive.

Day One Practice the following letters and words from this week's Scripture.

Nn

Never

within

instructions

Day Two Continue practicing letters and words from this week's Scripture.

Hh

Hold

truthful

heart

Kk

kind

satisfying

tightly

Day Four   Practice this week's entire Scripture verse by tracing over each of the words below.

If you want a long and satisfying life, closely follow My instructions. Never forget to be truthful and kind. Hold these virtues tightly. Write them deep within your heart.

Proverbs 3:2,3

FOR DISCUSSION

List some ways you can show kindness to your friends. . . your family. . .your neighbors. How does being kind make you feel inside?

Lesson 21

What two letters almost always go together?
(Hint: you have to be "quick" to get this!) As you practice the
qu combination this week, think of other words that use this combination.

Day One   Practice the following letters and words from this week's Scripture.

Li

Lt

despises

begin

Day Two   Continue practicing letters and words from this week's Scripture.

Qq

quarrel

starts

bad

Oo

once

stop

those

It is hard to stop a quarrel
once it starts, so don't let it begin.
The Lord despises those who say
that bad is good, and good is bad.
Proverbs 17:14,15

FOR DISCUSSION

What are some ways to stop a quarrel from beginning? In what way can our character help prevent quarrels?

Name _____

TIP OF THE WEEK

Focus on letter spacing and letter size
this week. Consistency in these two skills helps give
your handwriting a balanced look, and makes it easier to read.

Day One Practice the following letters and words from this week's Scripture.

Ss

spirit

sick

does

Day Two Continue practicing letters and words from this week's Scripture.

Mm

medicine

makes

good

Uu

but

cheerful

broken

Day Four Practice this week's entire Scripture verse by tracing over each of the words below.

A cheerful heart does good like medicine, but a broken spirit makes one sick.

Proverbs 17:22

FOR DISCUSSION

What are some outward signs of a cheerful heart? What might show a broken spirit? How should we respond when we see these signs in others?

Name _____

TIP OF THE WEEK

The capital letters *E, J,* and *C* are our focus this week.
Think of the name of a person or place that begins with each
of these letters. Just for fun, practice writing these names as well as others.

Day One Practice the following letters and words from this week's Scripture.

Ee

sense

ever

reputation

Day Two Continue practicing letters and words from this week's Scripture.

Zz

Zion

want

judgment

Cc

completely

common

trust

Day Four   Practice this week's entire Scripture verse by tracing over each of the words below.

If you want favor with both
God and man, and a reputation
for good judgment and common
sense, then trust the Lord
completely; don't ever trust
yourself.
Proverbs 3:4,5

FOR DISCUSSION
In order to really trust someone, you have to know them very well. What are some of the ways we can get to know God better?

TIP OF THE WEEK

This verse contains all the lowercase loop letters.
As you write the words, make certain you only place loops
where they belong. Also, review your posture and paper position this week.

Day One Practice the following letters and words from this week's Scripture.

L l

loving

gold

esteem

Day Two Continue practicing letters and words from this week's Scripture.

R r

rather

riches

silver

Day Three — Practice the final letters and words from this week's Scripture.

Hh

held

choose

must

Day Four — Practice this week's entire Scripture verse by tracing over each of the words below.

If you must choose, take a good name rather than great riches; for to be held in loving esteem is better than silver and gold.

—Proverbs 22:1

FOR DISCUSSION

How do our actions affect what others think of us? Does our relationship with God impact our behavior? In what way?

Name _____

TIP OF THE WEEK

To drive a car properly, you have to keep it
between the lines! Handwriting alignment is a lot like that.
Take extra care this week to keep your letters and words between the lines!

Day One   Practice the following letters and words from this week's Scripture.

Bb

but

by

mirror

Day Two   Continue practicing letters and words from this week's Scripture.

Ss

shown

friends

reflects

Yy

really

what

chooses

Day Four Practice this week's entire Scripture verse by tracing over each of the words below.

A mirror reflects a man's face, but what he is really like is shown by the kind of friends he chooses.

—Proverbs 27:19

FOR DISCUSSION

Think about your closest friends. What are they really like? How is this similar to or different from what you'd like to become?

Few verses contain *n* words, yet the *n* is still
an important letter to practice! Proverbs 4: 8, 9 is similar to this
week's verse, so we borrowed an *n* word from it for our practice this week.

Day One   Practice the following letters and words from this week's Scripture.

Pp

Proverbs

happy

keeps

Day Two   Continue practicing letters and words from this week's Scripture.

Dd

Wisdom

who

eating

Xx

exalt

tree

fruit

Day Four   Practice this week's entire Scripture verse by tracing over each of the words below.

Wisdom is a tree of life to those who eat her fruit; happy is the man who keeps on eating it.
Proverbs 3:18

FOR DISCUSSION
List some ways we can "eat" wisdom. What is the difference between wisdom and knowledge?

Name _____

 **TIP OF THE WEEK**

The overstroke is easy to identify in letters
like *n* and *m*. Watch for other overstroke letters as you
practice this week. (Hint: Four are in this verse, and two are not.)

Day One Practice the following letters and words from this week's Scripture.

Li

conceited

will

health

Day Two Continue practicing letters and words from this week's Scripture.

Nn

turn

renewed

given

Vv

evil

reverence

vitality

Day Four   Practice this week's entire Scripture verse by tracing over each of the words below.

Don't be conceited, sure of your own wisdom. Instead, trust and reverence the Lord, and turn your back on evil; when you do that, then you will be given renewed health and vitality.

— Proverbs 3:7,8

FOR DISCUSSION

Proverbs 16:18 offers additional insight into this topic. Describe its similarities to this week's verse.

Name _____

TIP OF THE WEEK

This verse contains the lowercase
tail letters *f, g, j, p,* and *y*. As you write,
make certain that you extend all these letters to the lower line.

Day One   Practice the following letters and words from this week's Scripture.

W w

We

pleased

gifts

Day Two   Continue practicing letters and words from this week's Scripture.

J j

justify

just

fair

Day Three   Practice the final letters and words from this week's Scripture.

Mm

motives

Him

more

Day Four   Practice this week's entire Scripture verse by tracing over each of the words below.

We can justify our every deed but God looks at our motives. God is more pleased when we are just and fair than when we give Him gifts.
Proverbs 21:2,3

FOR DISCUSSION
Can a person do something good for the wrong reasons? Why do our motives matter, anyway?

TIP OF THE WEEK

As you near the end of this year of Handwriting,
don't forget the importance of good posture! Your posture
has a direct impact on the consistency of letter and word slant.

Day One   Practice the following letters and words from this week's Scripture.

Ff

Follow

keep

advice

Day Two   Continue practicing letters and words from this week's Scripture.

Oo

Obey

possession

words

Uu

Guard

precious

live

Follow My advice . . . always keep it in mind and stick to it. Obey Me and live! Guard My words as your most precious possession.
Proverbs 7:1,2

FOR DISCUSSION

Name some specific advice from God that you can put into practice this week. In what way can we guard God's Word?

Name _____

TIP OF THE WEEK

Poor handwriting can cause some letters to be
mistaken for others. This week our focus is on the *h* and *k*.
Other letters easily mistaken for each other include *e-i, a-o, m-n,* and *y-g.*

Day One   Practice the following letters and words from this week's Scripture.

L l

Look

pull

safe

Day Two   Continue practicing letters and words from this week's Scripture.

K k

back

sidetrack

path

A a

ahead

straight

Watch

Look straight ahead; don't even turn your head to look. Watch your step. Stick to the path and be safe. Don't sidetrack; pull back your foot from danger.

— Proverbs 4:25, 27

FOR DISCUSSION

List some common things that might distract us from looking straight ahead and following God's path. How can we deal with these distractions? Be specific.

Name _____

TIP OF THE WEEK

Remember, your name is the most important
word you write. It should always be clear and legible.
(Someday when you're famous, we want to be able to read your signature!)

Day One   Practice the following letters and words from this week's Scripture.

Ii

wisest

life

you'll

Day Two   Continue practicing letters and words from this week's Scripture.

Mm

limp

stumble

run

D d

would

doing

fact

Day Four   Practice this week's entire Scripture verse by tracing over each of the words below.

I would have you learn this great fact: that a life of doing right is the wisest life there is. If you live that kind of life, you'll not limp or stumble as you run.
Proverbs 4:11,12

FOR DISCUSSION

List some attributes of right living. Name at least two good habits that you'd like to develop before next school year.

Name

TIP OF THE WEEK

This final Handwriting lesson is a good time to use the
Five Star evaluation once more. Compare your writing sample from
the beginning of the year with your writing today. Evaluate your progress.

Day One Practice the following letters and words from this week's Scripture.

Ww

When

worst

with

Day Two Continue practicing letters and words from this week's Scripture.

Gg

God

trying

please

Ee

enemies

even

peace

When a man is trying to please God, God makes even his worst enemies to be at peace with him.

Proverbs 16:7

For Discussion

Choose two character traits we've discussed this year that you'd like to improve this summer. Don't forget to ask God to help!

To The Teacher

The following pages are for use on Day 5 of the
Weekly Lesson Format (Teacher Guidebook, page 56).

These **Scripture Border Sheets** not only provide a
significant outreach component, but a strong
motivational tool as well.

This section contains 35 **Scripture Border Sheets** —
one per lesson, plus three different blanks (pages 139, 141
and 143) that allow for student-designed artwork.

For creative ways to use the **Scripture Border Sheets**
see "Ways to Share" (Teacher Guidebook, page 58).

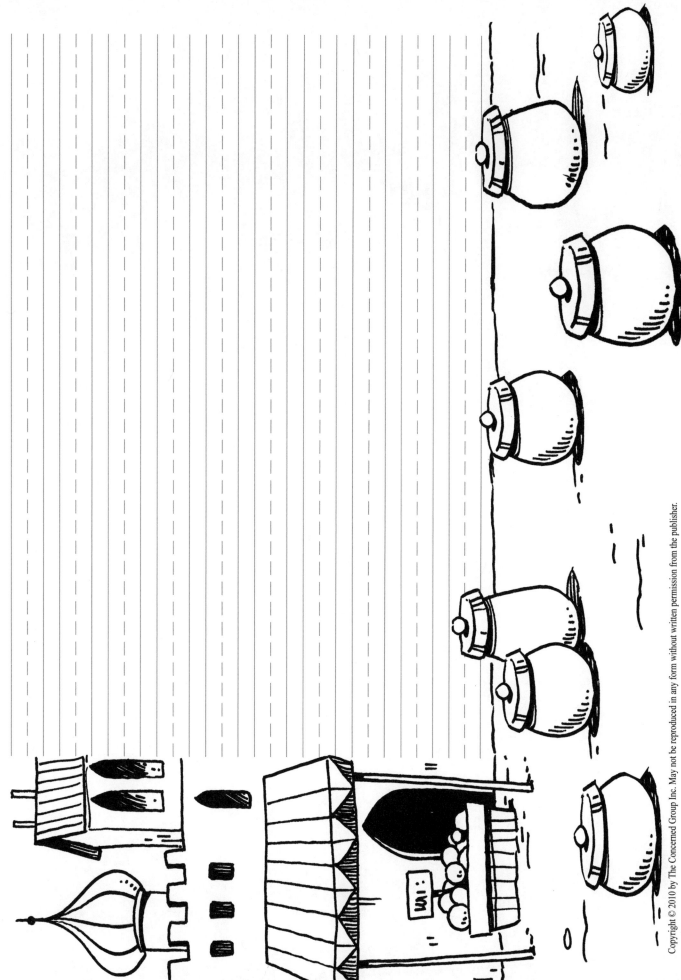

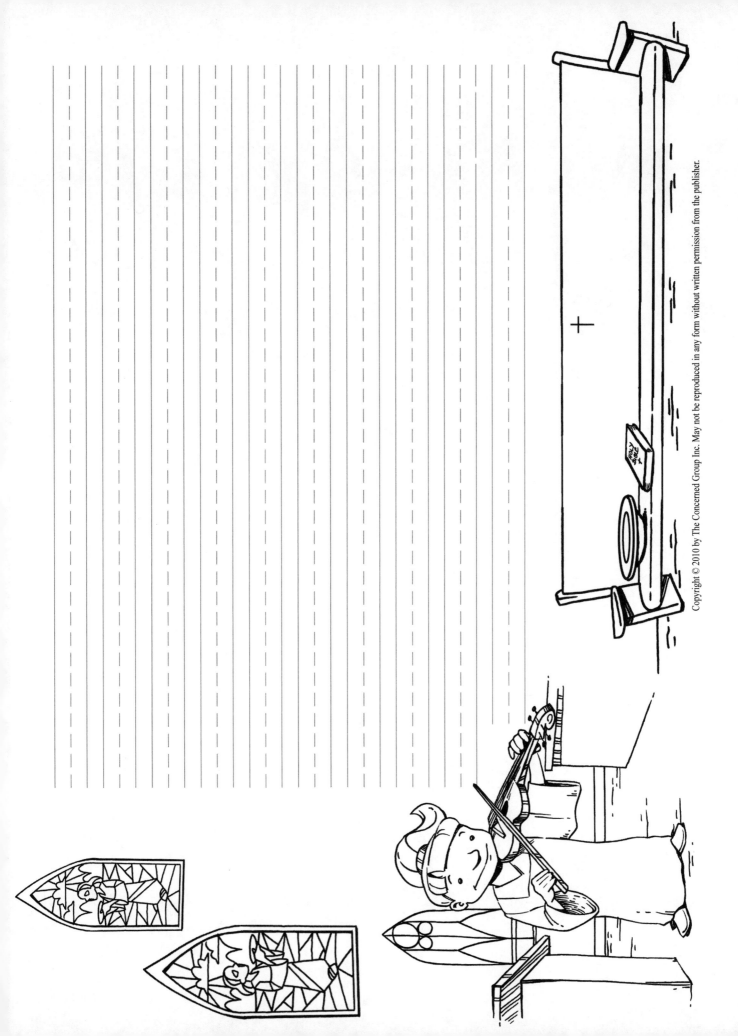

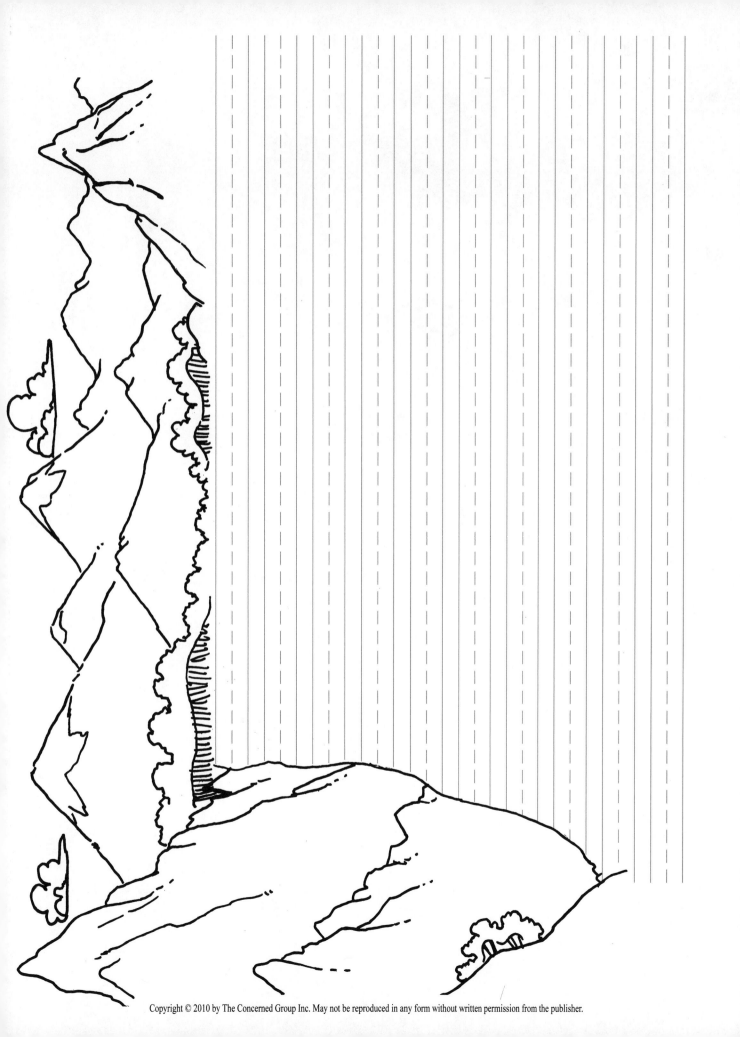

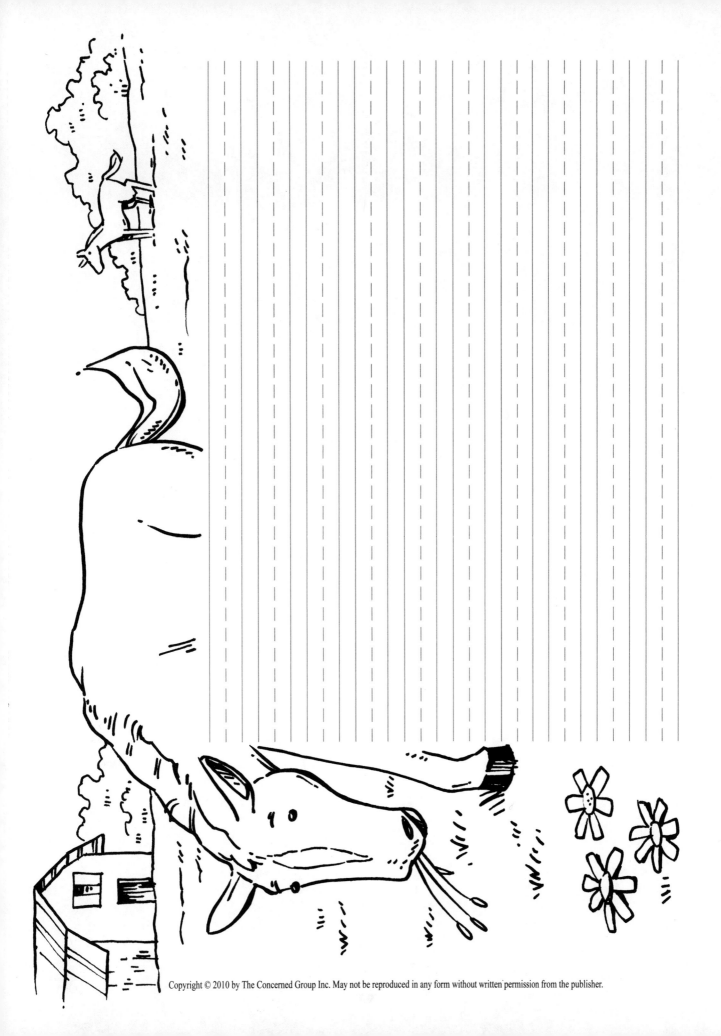

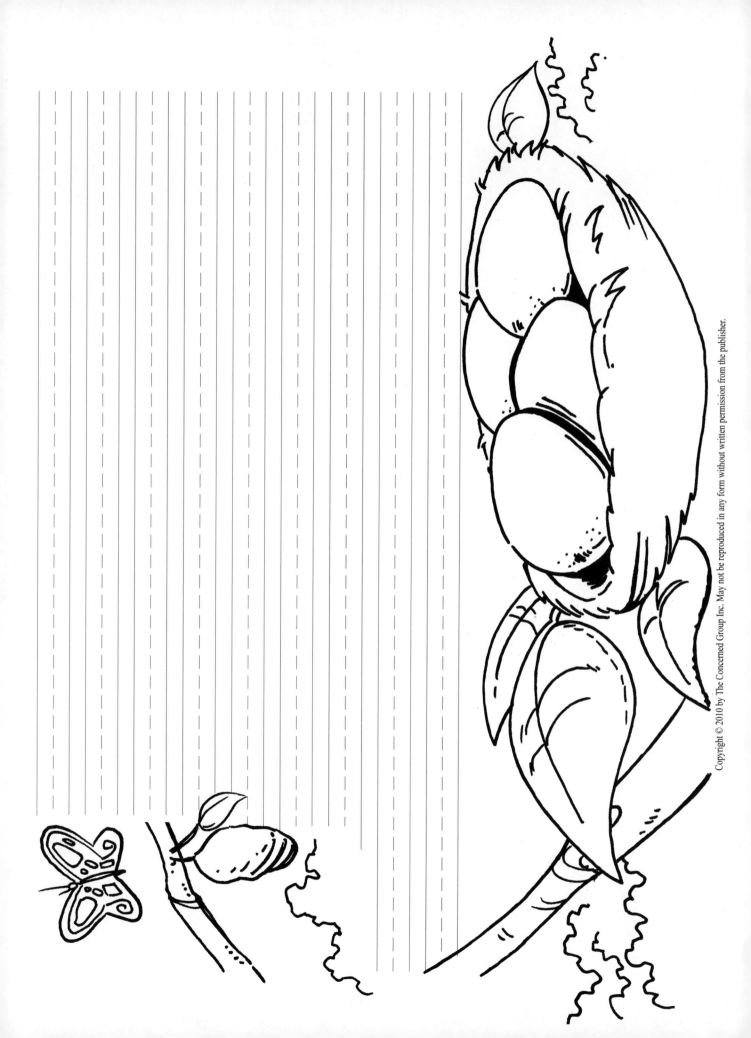

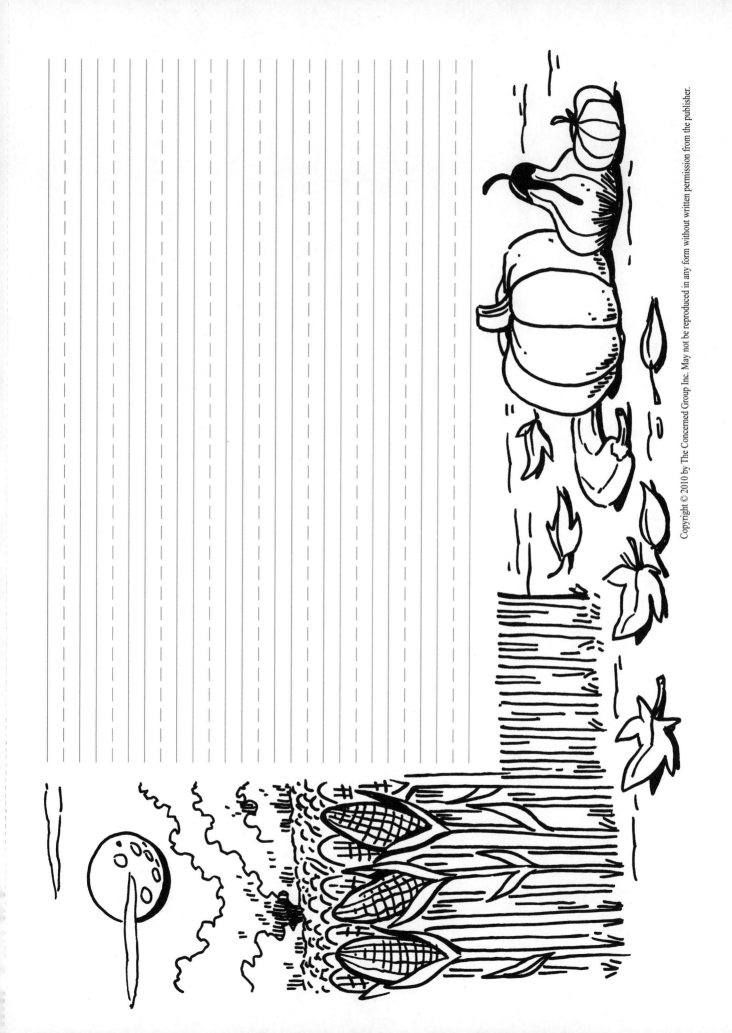

LEMONADE 50¢

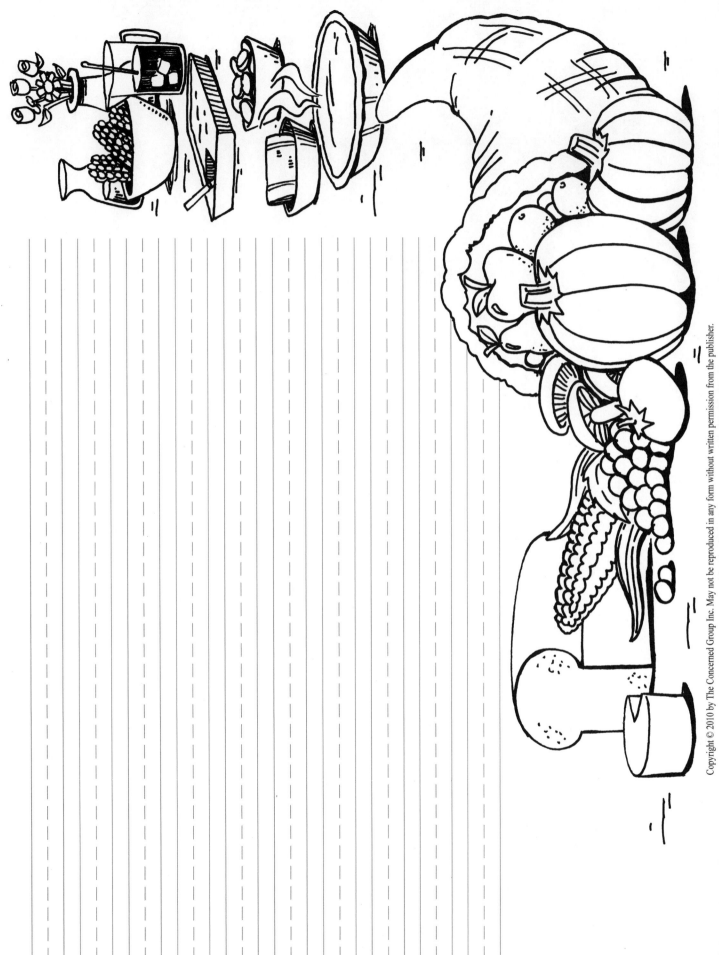

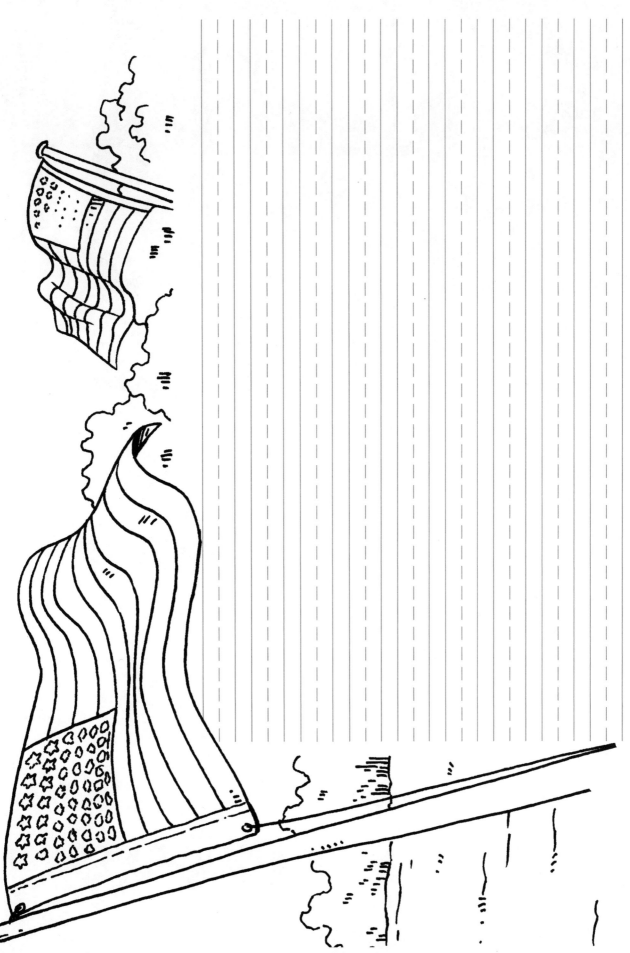

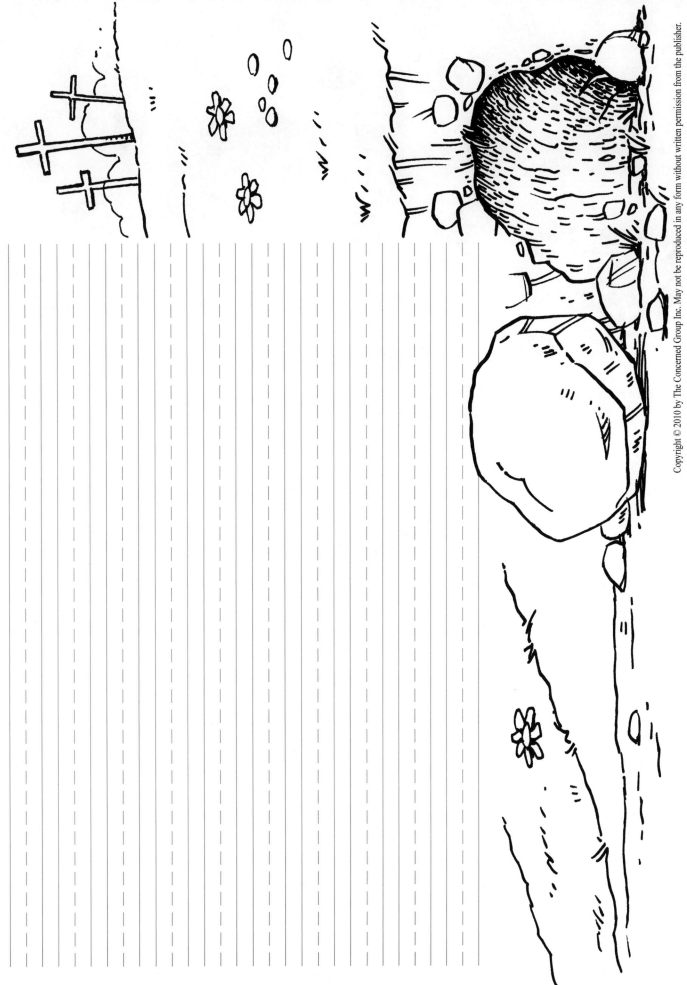